EMPOWERED

THE POWER OF WORDS

Edited By Allie Jones

First published in Great Britain in 2022 by:

Young Writers
Remus House
Coltsfoot Drive
Peterborough
PE2 9BF
Telephone: 01733 890066
Website: www.youngwriters.co.uk

Printed and bound in the UK by BookPrintingUK
Website: www.bookprintinguk.com
YB0496X

✶ FOREWORD ✶

Since 1991, here at Young Writers we have celebrated the awesome power of creative writing, especially in young adults where it can serve as a vital method of expressing their emotions and views about the world around them. In every poem we see the effort and thought that each student published in this book has put into their work and by creating this anthology we hope to encourage them further with the ultimate goal of sparking a life-long love of writing.

Our latest competition for secondary school students, Empowered, challenged young writers to consider what was important to them. We wanted to give them a voice, the chance to express themselves freely and honestly, something which is so important for these young adults to feel confident and listened to. They could give an opinion, share a memory, consider a dilemma, impart advice or simply write about something they love. There were no restrictions on style or subject so you will find an anthology brimming with a variety of poetic styles and topics. We hope you find it as absorbing as we have.

We encourage young writers to express themselves and address subjects that matter to them, which sometimes means writing about sensitive or contentious topics. If you have been affected by any issues raised in this book, details on where to find help can be found at
www.youngwriters.co.uk/info/other/contact-lines

★ CONTENTS ★

Academy @ Worden, Leyland

Ione Prescott (14)	1
Leon Calwell (12)	2
Olivia Deverson-Davies (11)	4
Katie Thompson (12)	6
Daisy Walsh (11)	8
Patrycja Brzozowska (12)	9
Connor Scott (11)	10
Wiktoria Raczek (12)	11
Lia Helyar (12)	12
Ruby Roscoe (12)	13
Maddie Briers (11)	14
Poppy Kershaw (11)	15
Liam Casey (12)	16
Alfie McFarlane (11)	17
Nikita Craven (11)	18
Bethany Kay (11)	19
Nathan Smith (12)	20
James Clayton-Bromiley (11)	21
Milly Robinson (11)	22
Jake Farrimond (11)	23
Millie Lythgoe (11)	24

Ballyclare High School, Ballyclare

Duncan Newell (15)	25
Amie Reid (17)	26

Burgess Hill Girls, Burgess Hill

Phoebe Millford (12)	28
Amelie Crabb	30
Miri Clarke (12)	32
Isabella Collins	33
Matilda Shilton (11)	34

Franchesca Burbidge	35

Cecil Jones Academy, Southend-On-Sea

Lilyana Chubb (11)	36
Sydney Atkin (12)	37
A Ha (11)	38
Ben Kasparian (11)	39
Tamzin Wilson (11)	40
Maddison Palmer	41
Ruby Fidgeon (12)	42
Theodore Pearcey (11)	43
Noah Harpaul-Knight (11)	44
Aimee Stear-Ellis (12)	45
Carter Brown (12)	46

Crofton School, Stubbington

Emily Pennington (13)	47
Poppie-Alice Crassweller (15)	48
Lillia Youngman (15)	50
Charlotte Farnsworth (12)	52
Ruby Davies (12)	55
A Vaughan	56
Sophia Worthy (11)	58
Phoebe Dickerson	60
Emily Downs (12)	62
Sofia Patap (11)	64
Emily Hunns (11)	66
Harry Head	67
Oluwadamilola Akinpelu (13)	68
A Tunstall	69
Alexandra Miller (13)	70
Emily Prest (12)	71
Esme Shepherd (12)	72

Jasmine Lummis (12)	73
Ahaan Sood (11)	74
F Lowe	75
Tyler Cull (12)	76
Joseph Ashcroft (13)	77
Kaylee Wightman (12)	78
Sophie Cromie (16)	79

De Lacy Academy, Knottingley

Dawid Mekarski	80
Olivia Spires (13)	82
Keira Clough (13)	83
Torin Irwin	84
Emelia Oldfield (11)	85
Dudzai Kuture (12)	86
Zain Mahmood (12)	87
Vidita Hakeem (13)	88
Alfie Steeples (13)	89
Mollie Jo Chapman (12)	90
Reuben Holden-Clough (13)	91
Jayden Bailey (13)	92
Callum Raynor (12)	93
Natalia Mekarska	94
Erin Norton (11)	95
Sophie Benn (13)	96
Lewis Clark (13)	97
Ellie Green (11)	98
Courtney Blakeston (13)	99
Lilly Myers (12)	100
Bailey Smith (11)	101
Caitlyn Lowe (14)	102
Cobi Pearson	103
Ellisha Sykes (12)	104
Jessica Wood (12)	105
Thomas Clarke (11)	106
Abigail Mitchell (13)	107
Sophie Spence-Hirst (13)	108
Lennon Hicks (11)	109
Kieran Halligan (12)	110
Riley Deakin (13)	111
Colby Platt (11)	112
Alfie Thompson (13)	113

Edgbarrow School, Crowthorne

Isobelle Hennessey (14)	114
Isabel Groves (11)	116
Caitlin Hickey (13)	118
Anwyn Howley (13)	119
Abigail Turner (12)	120
Meah Godwin (11)	121
Anya Agarwal (11)	122

Energy Coast UTC, Lillyhall

Derren Tyson (14)	123
Ruby Haile (14)	124
Callum Bell (14)	126
Alfie Cape (13)	127
Oliver (14)	128
Gracie (14)	129
Bobby Ennis (14)	130

Highcliffe School, Highcliffe

Hannah Hughes (14)	131
Alex Hughes (11)	132

Highshore School, Camberwell

Ashea Letts	134
Molly Grealish (16)	135
Tiarnie Porter (16)	136
Harry Lorraine-Grimes (16)	137
Annabelle Allen (14)	138
Casey	139

Magherafelt High School, Magherafelt

Alana Forsythe (16)	140
Chantelle Logan (16)	142
Lucy Arrell (13)	144
Grace McCormick (13)	146
Maisy Lee (12)	148
Gail Huey (13)	149
Leah McFadden (13)	150
Ethan Wilson (12)	152

Tyler Smyth (13) 153
Matthew Linton (12) 154
Grace Jones (13) 155
Hollie Gilmour (16) 156
Ella Clark (12) 157
Sienna Smith (15) 158
Rose Nicholl (15) 159
Sophie Neill (13) 160

The Adeyfield Academy, Longlands

Eleni Marangos (11) 161
Robert Vinyard (14) 162
Jack Hart (11) 165
Jenna-May Botha (13) 166
William Douthwaite (13) 168
Samuel Lewis (13) 170
Rudy Jawara (11) 171
Layla Brown (13) 172
Isabel Fallon (11) 173
Nabila Khan (12) 174
Vanesa Bartko (11) 175
Jessica Hinks (11) 176
Amiyah Muzuka (11) 177
Mia Capri Newland (12) 178
Dylan Pankhurst (11) 179
Katie Childs (12) 180
Zarrah Ali (12) 181
Skye Payne (14) 182

THE POEMS

Our Reality

Darting eyes
Clutched keys
Make sure your maps are on
Hide all vulnerability
From little girls
We are taught we're prey
Long skirts, baggy jumpers
Keep the problem at bay
We live in fear
We must pay
For the lost lives of women taken away
I will not live my life in fear
The teaching of acceptance must end here
We must fight for our safety, our comfort
No more blood
No more disappearance
No more silence
Together we make a stand
Our sisters, our mothers, our daughters
The little girl
She will walk in confidence that she is not a statistic
Feminine, bold, opinionated
We fight now
To make her future
Safe.

Ione Prescott (14)
Academy @ Worden, Leyland

I Am Empowered

E nergy
M otivated
P ersistence
O wnership
W orthwhile
E pic
R eady
M entality
E nthralling
N ow
T hriving

E nergy - I have the energy and strength to stay strong even when things are going bad.

M otivated - I'm ready to do this and tackle whatever challenges are in front of me.

P ersistence - I will keep working for my goals and not stop.

O wnership - I am my own leader, I am taking responsibility for myself, my own feelings and the direction of my life.

W orthwhile - I will spend my time and energy on things that are worthwhile, things that help me and the others around me.

E pic - I wish my life to be epic. I strive to be good, awesome or possibly even amazing.

R eady - I am ready, I am prepared, eager to start.

M entality - I have a positive mental attitude, happy thoughts.

E nthralling - I can become enthralled, an ability to concentrate and focus on one certain thing, temporarily spellbound by my surroundings or activities.

N ow - I take action now, focus on the here and now.

T hriving - I am raring to go, trying my best and doing well.

Leon Calwell (12)

Academy @ Worden, Leyland

No More Room On The Bookshelf

Books on the bookshelf,
Books all around!
Oh no it's almost bedtime!
But I just need to see what happens next,
Please let me stay up and read, Mother, please!

Books make me happy,
Books make me sad,
Books are a pinch of magic you can hold in your hand!

Let's buy another book! I've just finished this one!
Oh no! There's no more room on the bookshelf!
Oh what to do,
I know! I'll put them in the box!

Books make you feel powerful,
Books make you calm,
Books make you feel empowered,
Books can make you feel anything you want!

Let's buy another book! I've just finished this one!
Oh no! There's no more room on the bookshelf!
Oh what to do,
I know! I'll put them in the box!

Reading from dawn till dusk,
I just need to find out what happens next,
Just one more page and then I'll sleep,
But I need to see what'll happen next!

Let's buy another book! I've just finished this one!
Oh no! There's no more room on the bookshelf!
Oh what to do,
I know! I'll put them in the box!

Olivia Deverson-Davies (11)
Academy @ Worden, Leyland

Cornering The Catcaller

Walking down the street,
a cold winter's night.
Wrapped up in a hoodie,
not expecting a fright.

A noise behind,
my hairs standing on end.
Shivers down my spine,
who was it and what did they intend?

I steadily turned around,
not knowing what I would see.
There a man stood,
at least 2 feet taller than me.

I felt empowered,
a feeling came over my head.
I felt heroic and brave,
not fretting whatever came ahead.

Courage and courageous,
compassion and confidence.
All the things I felt,
this act didn't need experience.

Stepping forward,
I asked for him to leave me alone.

This man started harassing me,
and all I wanted was to go home.

Don't be afraid to stand up to people,
feel empowered like me.
Don't let them get the best of you,
you deserve to be free.

Katie Thompson (12)
Academy @ Worden, Leyland

Wonderful Worden

At first I was so scared,
But I came prepared.

Leaving old friends was sad,
But in the end it wasn't so bad.

The teachers I met were so kind,
I couldn't get them out of my mind.

I thought all of the pupils were friendly too,
I hope they all knew.

After a while I got used to it,
But I still missed primary a bit.

I can't wait to spend the next 5 years here,
Hopefully my worries will disappear.

So far I love my new school,
I will make sure I follow every rule.

Worden is the best high school ever,
I will remember it forever.

Daisy Walsh (11)
Academy @ Worden, Leyland

Another Way

I'm happy you're gone,
I feel healthy and free,
You made me feel like something was wrong,
Slapping layers of blindfolds on me,
You didn't want me to see,
The truth that was underneath.

What was coated on top was your lies,
I fell for them for a long time,
I gave you chances and tries,
It almost felt like a crime,
I was tired and sick of it,
Everything you said was a trick.

But you don't control me,
I've turned away,
Now you beg and plea,
Hoping I'll once again stay,
The experience was a maze,
But I've finally found another way.

Patrycja Brzozowska (12)
Academy @ Worden, Leyland

![YoungWriters Est. 1991]

A Charity Close To My Heart

This is about a charity close to my family and a condition my grandma had and my auntie still has.

M uscle-wasting condition,
U nheard of by many,
S uffering from this,
C ure I hope will come,
U nderfunded,
L ana, my auntie, is so brave,
A ll our time goes into this...
R aising money for this cause,

D reaming up many ways to raise awareness,
Y oung and old get involved,
S kydives, Snowdonia mountain and more,
T his was the start of it all,
R affles, hampers, started small,
O vercoming fears,
P eople helping out,
H eading for our target,
Y ou can make a difference!

Connor Scott (11)
Academy @ Worden, Leyland

The Best Professor

I felt empowered
And for me you were the source
To the front you always led
Saying the stage is yours
Though it was hard for me to stand
And to be noticed by all the class
But you made me understand
The courage is needed to progress

You knew exactly the right way
To show the girl who used to hide
I still recall my yesterday
I was your student, you were my guide
You teach, you help, you support too
And here I am passing the test
Of all the professors that I knew
You are definitely the *best!*

Wiktoria Raczek (12)
Academy @ Worden, Leyland

I Am Me

Why would I want to be someone else
when nothing is better than being myself?
No good pretending I'm someone else
when I've got something they haven't got.

Much more to offer with my own views
rather than walking round in someone else's shoes.
Living the life of others can be a mistake
in the end being found to be fake.

To people who know you, you're a bright shining star
to them it is obvious you will go far.
Follow your heart and your dreams will come true
feel empowered by just being you!

Lia Helyar (12)
Academy @ Worden, Leyland

Climate Change

C arbon dioxide fills the air,
L ife on Earth is just not fair,
I f we just acted differently,
M aybe the world would be magnificent.
A nother chance that's all we need,
T o show the world to believe,
E veryone can achieve.

C hange the world,
H and over a life pearl,
A nd give the world you (the saviour),
N ever stop believing,
G et to achieving,
E veryone stop disbelieving.

Ruby Roscoe (12)
Academy @ Worden, Leyland

Me And Myself!

My name is Maddie,
and I'm 11 years old,
I love warm weather,
but not the cold!

My hobbies include,
dancing and drums,
I enjoy school,
But not doing sums!

My weekends I spend,
Making a cake,
My favourite food is,
Pasta bake!

My family includes,
My sisters and dog,
We like to call her,
Our puppy frog!

So here's the end,
Don't judge me,
Be yourself,
And let people be!

Maddie Briers (11)
Academy @ Worden, Leyland

What Is It To Be You?

What is it to be you?
To be you then you need to be confident
To be you then you need to be kind
Then you are you.

What is it to be you?
To be you then you need to be loving
To be you then you need to be a loyal friend
Then you are you.

What is it to be you?
To be you then you need to be good fun
To be you then you need to be optimistic
It's great to be you!

Poppy Kershaw (11)
Academy @ Worden, Leyland

Self-Confidence

You are like a star in the sky,
You are one in a million.
You are beautiful,
You are smart.

As you can see,
All of these begin with you.
Not them, *you*.
You are the one everyone needs.
Don't care about what anyone thinks,
Be you and don't let anyone stop you.
Do what you want when you want,
You are unstoppable
You are the best.

Liam Casey (12)
Academy @ Worden, Leyland

The Boy Who Loves Football

Football is the game I love,
I like to watch and play.
Sometimes we play at home,
Sometimes we play away.

When I am on the wing,
I go off and spring.
Sometimes I put the ball in the goal,
Sometimes I take a fall.

Football is a game of speed,
It's a game that's full of skill.
A game that gives you a thrill.

Alfie McFarlane (11)
Academy @ Worden, Leyland

Interested?

Inspirational to me means being creative or spiritual,
Enthusiastic, exciting, make it your ritual.

Interested?

Don't be disheartened by every fall,
Remember, keep trying to reach your goal.

Push through your challenges and believe in yourself,
Don't try to be anyone else...

Interested?

Nikita Craven (11)
Academy @ Worden, Leyland

My Family

My parents, my brothers and sisters are my family.
They always build me up, when I am down
They're like my closest friends and they have their secret
space in my heart.

Why would I want anything different than my own family?
Nothing beats them
I'll love my family for life and after.

Bethany Kay (11)
Academy @ Worden, Leyland

I Can't Be Stopped

I won't be stopped,
I can't be topped,
My confidence won't be dropped,
I don't stop,

Nothing can beat me,
Nothing can defeat me,
I will stand strong,
No one can prove me wrong,

Nothing gets in my way,
On this day,
I will stay,
On top.

Nathan Smith (12)
Academy @ Worden, Leyland

I Feel Empowered

That's a good feeling
I feel big and strong
confident and worthy to say what I think
claiming my right in this world

It's time to seize your moment
and show the best of who you are
don't think about what they say
because at the end of the day we are equal.

James Clayton-Bromiley (11)
Academy @ Worden, Leyland

You Are You!

When all of your emotions build up,
Don't forget, never give up,
Persevere when you are stuck,
Then you will have good luck,
If you look,
You will see,
That every part of you is unique!

Milly Robinson (11)
Academy @ Worden, Leyland

The Phoenix

When you feel things are not going your way
Just remember all that is good
Don't fall into the ashes
Rise up with the flames
Like a phoenix burning brightly glistening like a star.

Jake Farrimond (11)
Academy @ Worden, Leyland

Smile

Being happy is fun
being sad is not
your smile is as bright as the sun
your frown is as dark as the moon
when you smile my heart goes boom
I love you.

Millie Lythgoe (11)
Academy @ Worden, Leyland

Drumming

D rumming is the most exhilarating activity any person can partake in,

R udiments are the backbone of every drummer's talent,

U nites people from around the world to get up and dance.

M ake new friends who enjoy playing marvellous music,

M ake new music with your new friends,

I always knew I would be empowered when behind my creative zone,

N ever thought I would be the person who I am today without drums,

G oing live and controlling the crowd is the most empowering feeling.

Duncan Newell (15)

Ballyclare High School, Ballyclare

Book-Smart Rebellion

I have always been 'the smart one',
always got the perfect grade.
But they used my brain as a loaded gun
to make sure others were afraid.

They twisted my ability
into a prize that they could win.
I became a number, a facility,
a robot wrapped in skin.

But robots have emotions,
maybe they forgot!
So, I gave up on devotions
and did what they could not.

I used the brain they weaponised
And started thinking my own thoughts.
And saw the people they had demonised
were not as wrong as I was taught.

Individual thinkers,
women with a voice,
they removed my blinkers,
they gave me a choice.

The choice to open up my eyes,
and see what I might find
when I don't allow some foolish guise
to steal the brilliance of my mind.

Amie Reid (17)

Ballyclare High School, Ballyclare

Time To Save Our Planet

I know that no one owns this planet,
But do you know
Whose job it is,
To keep the flow of rivers,
And ensure the water is unpolluted,
So innocent fish don't suffer slaughter?

Perhaps your clever little mind,
Shall, with urgent haste, assume,
There surely must be someone here,
That shows trust in wildlife.
And I suppose you think,
They mindfully wash,
All of climate change away!

Maybe now this is in writing,
You might just change your mind,
For it's your job,
And, yes, it's my one too,

To be kind with our world,
To be careful with our world,
To be mindful with our world,
To be true with our world,

I shall still be pleased,
Even if, you thought just for a minute,

About the damage we've already done,
And I truly do dare say,
All the things we can do to fix it.

So next time you find yourself,
Staring at an unkind piece of plastic,
Watching as,
The fantastically sized waves engulf it!
Or acknowledging yourself taking,
Your fifth piece of (unneeded) paper.
Ask why?
Do you actually know?
Don't sigh and move on,
Try acting on it,
Let's unite,
Join the fight,
Because it's...

Time to save our planet.

Phoebe Millford (12)
Burgess Hill Girls, Burgess Hill

The Perfect World

What if everything we know is a hoax
And every day we're haunted by the wraiths of mistake?
A friend
A foe
What if it's all the same
And there's no pain?
The perfect world.

The catastrophic events of our past
Push us to the breaking point
But in the perfect world
There'd be no misfortune.

Scrambling aggravated towards the light
We have to fight to see it
And although there is might
There's always the problem of scheming.

No racism would show
All genders the same
But it would glow if we had
The perfect world.

Coronavirus a plagiarism of safety
The Government a broken voice box
Spewing out useless knowledge.

When words cut us down
And you can't fly
Remember that I believe

No evil or profanity
Or crying hard in agony
In the perfect world.

Amelie Crabb

Burgess Hill Girls, Burgess Hill

Our Earth Deserves Better

Our Earth deserves better.
Much better than what it's got.
Think of others' futures.
Our future.
Your future.
Your legacy.
We, together, can make a difference
Just make a start.
You want our planet to thrive.
I want our planet to thrive.
You want beauty and happiness.
You are squeezing out every last drop of life.
We shall come to a catastrophic conclusion.
The wraith of the world will disappear into nothing.
The pirates of the oblivion will dominate the universe.
They'll dominate your life.
So try.
Please try.
For the sake of the world.
But hurry.
The sand has almost run out.

Miri Clarke (12)
Burgess Hill Girls, Burgess Hill

Nobby

Jumping with joy and excitement he prepared
himself into a bubbling canter towards the first jump
and soared over it like a dove blowing the crowd away!
He circled up to the second jump and charged towards it.
This time he felt pressure from the crowd,
He desperately wanted to please but
It was too much.
He stopped.
The crowd stood in aggravating silence. Nobby felt deep
shame.
He'd let me down. With doubt we circled and tried again
He did the best he could
and soared over the jump!
The crowd went wild!

Isabella Collins
Burgess Hill Girls, Burgess Hill

Make Change Happen

Whether it is boys or girls
They all go through the same
They are going through grief
And this is now my aim:

Help the people on the streets
They are out there in the cold,
They're alone and starving
Stand with me and be bold.

We need to help
We can't leave them there
They are starved and poor
Come on let's do a dare:

I dare you to be strong
I dare you to be bold
I dare you to talk
Before we get too old.

Matilda Shilton (11)
Burgess Hill Girls, Burgess Hill

Sound

Blue, red, green, yellow
Scrambling together
Yet you cannot see it,
And you cannot feel it,
Swirling, twirling, dancing
Creating colours and
Luminous effects yet you still cannot see it.
It is a form of sight created not by eyes,
But by the listeners, the ears.
The image they create,
Different to any other sense
Makes something beautiful.

Franchesca Burbidge
Burgess Hill Girls, Burgess Hill

Empowered Poem

You are my sunshine, your love makes me feel welcomed
You helped me up when I fell down
Sat with me when I cried
If you weren't here, I think I would die

You inspired me
Gave me advice when I really needed it
When I'm down
You're always here to make my frown go upside down

Wiped my tears away when I felt pain
You'll always remain
You love me for who I am
You're my toast to my jam

You always make me feel confident
And make me feel independent
You bring me strength
We'll have each other for a long length

You make me laugh every day
And will always be by my side
Till the day I die
And for that and everything
Thank you, thank you.

Lilyana Chubb (11)
Cecil Jones Academy, Southend-On-Sea

Bisexuality

Bisexuality
People say I'm bisexual
Because it's a craze
But that's not at all why

Bisexuality
I'm bisexual because of my feelings
It's about who I'm attracted to
I'm bisexual because,
I'm not just attracted to boys
I'm not just attracted to girls
I'm enchanted by both

People say it's teen spirit
Why don't they understand?
I'm not just attracted to boys
I'm not just attracted to girls
I'm enchanted by both

Bisexuality
It's not just a craze
It's not a trend at all
It's just how I feel
It's how we feel.

Sydney Atkin (12)
Cecil Jones Academy, Southend-On-Sea

To Someone Who Inspires Me

M y sister always makes me feel happy.
Y elling at each other is not something my sister does

B elieve in my sister and myself
E nding the arguments between us (my sister and myself).
S ensible is the right thing to me and my sister.
T rusting myself and my family

S top being angry to other people
I n life, I will completely change into a good person
S top being rude and silly to my family
T rying my best and never give up
E mpowered is what we want
R esting is good for your body, mind and soul.

A Ha (11)
Cecil Jones Academy, Southend-On-Sea

Be Yourself

B elieve you can and you will complete that goal.
E xpress yourself.

Y ou're perfect, don't worry about what they think.
O rganise yourself for every challenge.
U sually you would doubt yourself, but that stops today.
R espect others and they will respect you.
S mile, keep your head up.
E very day is a new start.
L ove, laugh, live life.
F inally, remember to *be yourself!*

Ben Kasparian (11)
Cecil Jones Academy, Southend-On-Sea

Empowered

Dear future me,
Promise me one thing,
Follow your aspirations, however or whatever state you're in
And try to see through them.

Dear future me,
One thing to ask,
Be fearless
Be brave
No matter the situation.

Dear future me
I ask you one thing,
Remember to smile and laugh,
Be kind and happy behind the mask too.

Dear future me.
One final thing,
Don't be afraid to show your true colours,
Surround yourself with love,
That's it for now, good luck.

Tamzin Wilson (11)
Cecil Jones Academy, Southend-On-Sea

Will It Be Worth It?

Animals have no homes
Because of us humans they've been destroyed
For humans to have a home
Because of us humans
Our animals are dying
Because people are buying
Homes that are for our animals
To have as their own
The animals are all alone
Although it's banned
And poachers think it's right
You're killing our endangered animals
In plain sight
Soon they will be gone
And then due to no animals
Will it be worth it?
When we're all gone.

Maddison Palmer
Cecil Jones Academy, Southend-On-Sea

Baking Poem

Baking allows you to be creative
You can be imaginative
It allows you to be free,
When your family wants to try, all you get is a plea.
Have fun and relax
This is a time to chillax
Cakes, muffins and much more,
With customers knocking on your door,
This is what makes me feel empowered.

Oh sorry... I've got to go, the cookie dough needs to be floured!

Ruby Fidgeon (12)
Cecil Jones Academy, Southend-On-Sea

Me

As I stand before you
As I look around
I see a lot of faces
I hear a lot of sound

As I rise to a challenge
As I learn and grow
I stumble and I fall
I'm proud of what I know

As I step to my future
As I find my key
I don't know what it may bring
I can't wait to see

Standing tall
Standing strong
I know where I belong.

Theodore Pearcey (11)
Cecil Jones Academy, Southend-On-Sea

Empowered

E ncouraging to other people
M anaging the world around me
P owerful thoughts whizz around my head
O verwhelming life can be
W orthy is what I feel about myself sometimes
E xciting what life can bring
R eady to be
E ffective, accomplish what I need to be
D edicated to my life.

Noah Harpaul-Knight (11)
Cecil Jones Academy, Southend-On-Sea

Women

Hear me out, we need to talk,
Some women have rights,
Like they always should,
Some women don't,
Which makes no sense,
Aren't we all human?

You think something's wrong,
You've got to stand up,
Warning may not be hard,
Because you're female,
Just do it,
It's worth it.

Aimee Stear-Ellis (12)
Cecil Jones Academy, Southend-On-Sea

Empowerment Poem

You can be the star in your own sky,
Take a breath and make a wish off the shooting stars.
Be like the cow that jumped over the moon
And soon you will see yourself zoom,
You can make it to your dreams,
Your dreams,
Your dreams,
Oh yes you can.

Carter Brown (12)
Cecil Jones Academy, Southend-On-Sea

Powers Of The Year

The magic of growth is a gift to behold,
And this magic is the Earth's to hold.

Spring dawns bright and early,
Of course, this happens yearly,
Baby lambs are learning to walk,
And baby birds are beginning to talk.

Summer comes and with it fresh flowers,
That bloom all day and through all the hours,
But there is something about today,
That makes the grass glow in a special way.

Autumn is next, where the leaves fall,
Which means woodland fun for all,
People are collecting conkers from the ground,
So, they can plant them and watch them all year round.

Winter comes and so does a chill,
But it brings with it a certain thrill,
The time of Christmas has come,
Bringing all sorts of merry fun.

The magic of growth is a gift to behold,
And this magic is the Earth's to hold.

Emily Pennington (13)
Crofton School, Stubbington

A Bird

Just like a bird I'm stuck in a cage
People tell me this is just a phase
I'll grow out of this depressive stage...
But I know I won't, for like a bird my wings have been clipped
I constantly feel my mind slip
Just like Alice falling down the rabbit hole
Not knowing which way to go
Not knowing which path to take or which way is safe
Knowing each choice I take may make me break

It's exhausting
I'm so tired
This beast that lives within drains the life right from my bones
Oh god I just want to go home!
I want to run
I want to scream
I pray for this all to be some bad dream
But I know it's not
I know this beast will never rot
I know this beast
I have to face it every day of every week

This beast inside of me is far from weak
It's a monster that I'll never defeat

But every evil can be overcome
So this is a something that something has to be done

You may believe you are broken
You may think that you can never be woken
But you can
You are far from broken
You can be outspoken
You just have to believe that you can put yourself together again
Did Stephen King give up when faced with his drug and alcohol addiction then?
Did he decide it wasn't worth fulfilling his life?
No!
No he didn't, he broke free of the pain and look at him now
He became so strong, even I still wonder how
So you can fight too and make something new
You can win your battle that'll change the whole world

You are not a statistic in a chart
You are in so many people's hearts
And if you still don't believe me then look around at the world you live in
Look around at the faces of your friends and family, your life is just about to begin

There's a warrior deep within
And you are sure to win.

Poppie-Alice Crassweller (15)

Crofton School, Stubbington

School Life

It's Monday morning, I walk into school and all I hear is:
"Tuck in that shirt"
"You call that a skirt?"
"Don't be a twerp!"
"To be honest, I don't give a toot!" I blurt.

Life at school is a tiresome tradition,
It needs a wrecking ball and a demolition.

It's Tuesday as usual, the dinners make me feel sick.
There's always that one kid that thinks it's lit,
Wearing a cashmere knit.

Life at school is a tiresome tradition,
It needs a wrecking ball and a demolition.

Wednesday arrives, middle of the week.
Two more days and I can get out of this heap,
I'm sick of being surrounded by sheep.

Life at school is a tiresome tradition,
It needs a wrecking ball and a demolition.

Thursday, nearly the weekend, so near yet so far.
Two more years until I can hit the bar.
To all the teachers I'll shout, "Au revoir!"

Life at school is a tiresome tradition,
It needs a wrecking ball and a demolition.

Yes, it's Friday, almost the weekend.
Freedom nearly here time for a cheer, someone pass me a
root beer.
Let's get this party turned up a gear!

Life at school is a tiresome tradition,
It needs a wrecking ball and a demolition.

Lillia Youngman (15)
Crofton School, Stubbington

Help Me To Be Free Of This

Here I am
The bare bones of me,
Stripped of any false fantasies

Here you have it, the real me

Cold at times, but warm mostly
That heat is fading,
Support beams are failing,

I'm not what I used to be
I've had a taste of reality
I try so hard,
To be there

I've blown so many fuses,
I'm going crazy
But just maybe
There's a way to save me,
I just want my surgery
From Mr Davis

Let me rise once more,
Let me be there,
Let me be a phoenix

Let me be free of this
I just need my spine fixed

I want to be living life,
The real way
Not this,
Surreal way,

Can't get up,
Have to stay down,

Missing lessons
That can't come down

I just want to...
Do more,
Be more,
Be there for everyone,

I can't walk for long,
Not before the pain arrives
Nothing can stop it

I've fought it for so long,
It's mining away at me
Breaking me down

Till I'm a pile of rocks on the ground

I can't fight it for much longer,
It's at the door,
I only have one resort,

My wheelie machine
My wheelchair

Yeah,
I need a chair to be me

As I wheel round
I gain more control
I speed around school
I open my own doors now.

Charlotte Farnsworth (12)

Crofton School, Stubbington

I Open My Eyes To See

I open my eyes to see
A world of high expectations
Beauty, getting the latest iPhone
What's fashionable and what's not...

All of it's so overwhelming
Almost scary in fact
As if voices you can't shake
Are whispering in your ears
"Listen to us and you'll always be happy"

"Girls have to find their king, act like a little princess and
rock out in their shortest skirt," they say
"Guys have to find their place in the world, become strong
and brave, and save those damsels in distress," they say

But, maybe, just maybe, could there be an in-between?
What if I don't wanna find my prince?
But what if I don't want to conform?
Is there even an in-between?
What if I'm different?

Ruby Davies (12)
Crofton School, Stubbington

The Roller-Coaster Journey Of COVID!

In 2019 a change began,
Nobody even had a single plan
It started in China, with a little bat
It soon spread as quick as that

A continuous cough, high temperature, a sneeze
Loss of smell and taste as well
Everyone in fear
Waiting to see if COVID tests were clear

Around the world lockdown began
Now there seemed to be more of a plan
Businesses, schools, parks and pools shutdown,
Everywhere on pause with silence around

With more people getting ill
The world was worse again still
Hospitals too full
With staff really feeling the pull
Protect the NHS Boris Johnson said!

Vaccines came out
Meaning we could get about
Whilst remembering hands, face, space to keep us all safe

With things re-opening the excitement was true
COVID cases sadly increased and grew

Returning to lockdown we went again
All those feelings back they came
With daily updates becoming the norm
Panic buying returned - it was like a storm

Nearly two years on
It really has been so long
Vaccine boosters start up
Let's hope nothing has to shut
We hope the future is bright
As we might see the light...

A Vaughan
Crofton School, Stubbington

What Can You Do?

What can you do when there's litter on the streets?
What can you do when there's pollution in the air?
What will happen to this planet that we mistreat?
What will happen to the innocent animals' stare?

A stare of hope,
A glare of plead,
The question of will they cope?
The question of will you do your good deed?

Will you just sit there,
Switch on the TV,
Let the environment suffer in despair
And just watch the animals crying in plea?

What will happen when this planet goes to waste?
Its beautiful skirts of grass,
Its beautiful, luscious trees,
All gone apart from that feeling of guilt we must taste.

We'll all start to slowly perish,
After we kill the layer of soil that we walk upon,
Our land will no longer flourish,
Just because of our selfish greed that leaves everything gone.

Making this precious gem waste away,
Humankind are in a way murderers,
Counting all the precious trees that we slay
Before the world surrenders.

We can flick the switch,
Before it's too late
You can do your bit,
Before the Earth's lungs start to die.

Sophia Worthy (11)
Crofton School, Stubbington

Cursed Crystals

Inspired by 'Jabberwocky' by Lewis Carroll

'Twas twilight and the big grey moon,
Did glow and glimmer with stars,
All taken was the snoozin' noon,
And the neighbours had no chocolate bars.

Beware the crystals, my son,
The beauty that had, the power that kills,
Beware the curse they keep and shun,
The book of dark chills.

He took his hammered hammer in hand,
Long time the horrid foe he sought,
So rested he by the blossom tree,
And stood awhile in thought.

And, in deep thought he stood,
The cursed crystals with eyes of glass
Came flying through the shelves of wood,
And flame came, and passed.

One two, one two and through and through,
The hammered hammer went smicker-smack,
He left it dead and with its head,
He went saluting back.

'And hast thou slain the crystals cursed?
Come to my arms, my heroic boy!
Oh grateful day! Yahoo, yahay!'
He bounced in his joy.

'Twas twilight and the big grey moon,
Did glow and glimmer with stars,
All taken was the snoozin' moon,
And the neighbours had no chocolate bars.

Phoebe Dickerson
Crofton School, Stubbington

Reflection

I don't always find it easy to be myself.

Being myself.
Doing what I love without worrying about what other people think of me.

Sometimes I can't find the right words to say.
I can be quite quiet
So not many people know the real me

Who is the real me?
I can be funny
Creative
Caring
Thoughtful
Expressive
But I don't always show it

I work hard.
I achieve.
But I don't always believe in myself.

"When will my reflection show who I am inside?"
I sang and danced to this song in a festival and won a trophy
The adjudicator believed in me
The audience believed in me
So maybe I can too.

Being empowered is being able to feel confident and in
control
Without having to worry about anyone else.
I want the future me to believe this
And live with no limitations.

Emily Downs (12)
Crofton School, Stubbington

The World

The seasons are changing
And so is the world
And the way that it revolves.

The world is changing
Bit by bit
But we are doing everything we can
To help it.

Reducing pollution, recycling what we can
Cutting low on carbon
I know we can all do this!

Houses flooded, sea creatures fleeing
For their lives
That's the consequences
For all of this mess.

Our forests are turning to ash
Our factories are working,
And toxins emitting.

Our world is crumbling apart,
And we won't stop putting chemicals in the air
That we are trying to
Breathe!

But people are trying,
And people care,
But if this goes on for much longer,
I'm sad to say...

Dear 2065...
I don't think the world is
Going to be the same...

Sofia Patap (11)
Crofton School, Stubbington

Misunderstood

I'm misunderstood,
Nobody gets me at all.
Positive, negative, what to believe?
Your thoughts are all that matter.

I'll be there at Christmas,
Seeing smiles across children's faces,
Feeling like an outcast to all the other seasons.
Where did summer and spring go? Nobody knows.

Harmony is all I want,
I don't want it, I need it.

I have a dark side,
It only takes over when I want,
Not you or any other can take control,
It's me only me,
I decide if the bitter wind blows.

Now you sit there pleading for forgiveness,
Go, scram, don't waste your time here begging,
Go be with your friends and family,
I'm misunderstood,
I don't have a chance.

Emily Hunns (11)
Crofton School, Stubbington

Wake Up

Wake up to reality.
Nothing goes as planned in this accursed world
Emotions that whirl, swirl, and twirl
The longer a man lives the more he realises
The only things that truly exist in this world are negativity
Pain, suffering and futility
Pain.
Nothing to gain

Listen. Everywhere you look in this accursed world
Wherever there is light
There will always be shadow
As long as there is the concept of victors
The vanquished will also breed
When the selfish intent of wanting to preserve peace occurs,
Wars are sure to proceed
Hatred is born in order to protect love
Many simply just want to live

There are nexuses that cannot be separated
These imprison society.

Harry Head
Crofton School, Stubbington

Knowledge For The Heart

Life, Life! Life?
Where do you go?
How do you start?
I hate thinking too much,
thinking about the future.

I'd like to think of who people think of
Me
If I lived, died, survived
Who am I?
I know I'm Oluwadamilola Akinpelu
Of course, I know that
But truly who am I?
Nigerian?
British?
Hausa? Yoruba?
The girl across the road?
The girl who went to Crofton?
The doctor?
The runner?
I have so many questions
With no answers, leads, ends...

So please give my heart a plaster,
Please give my heart knowledge.

Oluwadamilola Akinpelu (13)
Crofton School, Stubbington

Empowered By School

I like being eleven,
I'm now in year seven
These past few years have been tough
Not going to lie, they have been rough

It's a new school year,
Now I'm trembling in fear
But making friends has been easy
And my school days have been breezy

I like my school so far,
My mum takes me in the car
I have lots of new things to learn
Finding my way around was a concern

My tutor is nice,
She gives good advice
Her name is Mrs Byford
She doesn't let us get bored

Crofton is a great school,
It welcomes all
We have gone from primary school to secondary school
And all the teachers are all wonderful.

A Tunstall
Crofton School, Stubbington

Empowered

We stand below a taunted body,
One stained with blood and burn marks that
Cannot be washed
No matter how hard their hands scrub at their skin, the
Blemishes stay, stubborn and stark.
Solitude unlocked. Self-recognition.
Fog clearing from our brains and smoothing out.
It was my eyes that searched out the faults
This time, that burnt a trail of scorn and anger.
Do we blame the time alone, or the time before?
Angry at those who were too slow, or those who
Wanted to go faster?
Is there truly a middle-ground in a battlefield?
Can you really call no-man's land peaceful?

Alexandra Miller (13)
Crofton School, Stubbington

What Do I Do?

I do get called;
A neek,
And a nerd
And a geek
And a smart girl and...
Why? Why me?
I do my work, I am ambitious, I am diligent

Do they need help?
Are they jealous?
Do they know jealousy is a sin?
I can help them!
But no! They don't want help from a neek like me,
No one does!

Going to school is intense
Even harder when,
You know there is nobody there to catch you when you fall,
Only silent screams
Even at the top of my lungs!
No one can hear.

I just don't get it!
What do I do?
Do I leave them or help them?
No one told me what to do.

Emily Prest (12)
Crofton School, Stubbington

We Can Succeed!

I bring beauty!
I bring peace!
I bring hope!

You have hurt me!
You made me sad!
You are killing me!

My beauty has faded!
My peace has gone!
I have no more hope!

Animals are suffering, their homes are no longer here!
All faith devoured into a whirlpool of disaster!

So stop and fix what you have done!
You must put me back together!
It will be tough, it will be hard but we can succeed!

So pick up some rubbish!
Turn off the lights!
And make some room for a better life!

For I am Earth!
And we only have one option

We can succeed!

Esme Shepherd (12)
Crofton School, Stubbington

A World Is A World

A world is a world
Filled with all types of humans and creatures
With all their wonderful features
Sun, sand, sea and earth we shall preserve them for all their
worth

Oh climate change! Oh climate change!
Don't you think things are strange?
Oh climate change! Oh climate change!
They are endangered
Along with their species.
Earth, you have lots of mountains
With such beautiful surroundings.
We all like you.
We love you too.

Jasmine Lummis (12)
Crofton School, Stubbington

A Poem About The Blitz

Siren wailing,
Bombs hailing,
Searchlights dotted,
Planes spotted.

Hoses sprayed a cure,
Fires dodged what was pure.
The destructive explosives dangerous like knives,
Anderson shelters saving lives.

German planes glided across the sky,
Bullets coming up from high.
The people sneaked,
Before they shrieked.

Dust gathered,
Fires bothered,
Andersons saved,
Bullets sprayed; many lives were lost.

Ahaan Sood (11)
Crofton School, Stubbington

Flowers

They have no mouths, but seem to speak
A thousand words so mild and meek.
They have no eyes, but seem to see
A sign of beauty
A symbol of grace
Its pride runs strong
At a very fast pace.
You might think
A bunch of plants
Aren't special
In any way
But,
Every flower has its own personality
As well as its own mentality
Tuck them into their originality
Beds full with soil.

F Lowe
Crofton School, Stubbington

I Don't Like School

I don't like school I tell my mum.

My friends aren't friends
They bully me and make fun.

I try to be nice and I try to have fun
But all the time they make me feel dumb.

I'm not a wuss or a double-decker bus,
I'm just Tyler trying to learn and have fun.

I don't like school I tell my mum.

Tyler Cull (12)
Crofton School, Stubbington

You

You! Yes, you!
You can make a difference.
It may be ignorance, but it's true.
The only hope we have is you.
I'm sorry if I sound stupid by saying this,
And you may feel mad, but
We will get through this.
We will not resist.
Be kind and you'll find
That all you need to do is be you!

Joseph Ashcroft (13)
Crofton School, Stubbington

Earth Is Shared

We can't do pollution
We need to save evolution
We need to be drastic and stop the plastic
Don't be dull and save the seagulls
Don't quarrel and save the coral
The oceans are full of beautiful creatures
Be a teacher and preach to the nation
To make the world a better place.

Kaylee Wightman (12)
Crofton School, Stubbington

My Dogs

Haiku poetry

Casey and Cara
Are playful, naughty and fun
They like to take toys!

Swimming in the sea
Their favourite thing to do
Shake all over me!

Always scrounge for food
They steal whatever they can
Biscuits, treats and bones!

Sophie Cromie (16)
Crofton School, Stubbington

Equality

Equal rights.
Something talked about every day.
We're born equal, all of us.
Some male, some female.
Some something in-between.
And some neither.
Some might become doctors.
Some might become police officers.
One's heart could be greyscale.
One's heart could be colourful.
So how does something so diverse, yet equal
Become a sinner and something inferior?

We all go on to enjoy different careers.
Yet how is it that two people working the same job,
Get wages of imbalance?
One could earn more than another.
It could be anything.
Veterinarian.
Butcher.
Retail worker.
Usually, nobody earns more than men.
So, how can it be something so diverse, yet equal?
Get put into a life of unfair rewards?

The change starts from you.
Even one person can change the world.
You need to be the change you wish to see.
So treat people equally.
So that something so diverse, yet equal.
Can once more feel completely equal.

Dawid Mekarski

De Lacy Academy, Knottingley

The World That A Book Contains

When I picked out a book,
And I took a look.
Before I knew it,
I had fallen into a pit.
Behind me was a doorway that was lit.

As I walked through the doorway,
There was a man collecting his pay,
There was a fish swimming through.
Then I heard a baby coo.
There was so much going on.

I looked back,
But the doorway was black.
I ran back into it.
And once again I fell into the pit.
I woke up with my head in the book,
It must have been a dream.
I yearn to be free like then.

But I know I can't because,
The library is shutting
And it's getting dark outside.
Books make me feel free,
They are a part of me.

Olivia Spires (13)
De Lacy Academy, Knottingley

Animal Abuse

A nimals are loving and caring creatures

N ot to be used for fighting, starving and beating.

I s that how you would like to be treated?

M ost likely not, so please help these pets by donating to shelters.

A nimals deserve to be happy and loved.

L ocking them in cages forever is not good.

A nimals like horses are often abused.

B ig Lick is a sport, in which horses are used.

U sed to carry heavy weights on their hooves, as well as bleach on their legs.

S top animal abuse by donating to shelters and if you see anyone abusing their pets, call the police.

E ducate children to help animals and never abuse them.

Keira Clough (13)
De Lacy Academy, Knottingley

Heroes Are Real

H ere many still think that heroes are not real.

E ven though they are.

R eal heroes may not be able to fly, but they still exist and they're not too far.

O thers may not see them but...

E verywhere

S till they stand

A ll around us and they do not demand.

R espect, attention or even a hand.

E ven giving advice to someone sad...

R eally can add to a person who is driven mad.

E ven thanking them can push them a mile.

A mbulance drivers, to the ER

L idl, Aldi, Morrisons and more. They are all great.

But most of all, thank you NHS.

Torin Irwin
De Lacy Academy, Knottingley

Dreams

Close your eyes, shut your mouth.
Imagine a wonderful world,
North, east, west and south.

A world where climate change isn't occurring,
Or a world where the virus isn't happening.

Where you find the luck of a four-leaf clover.
And wish for your dreams to never be over.

You could be relaxing on the warm beach sand,
Oh, your dreams could be a wonderland!

Your dreams can be a truly wonderful thing.
A place of fun, where you can dance and sing!

Then you open up your eyes, your dream has finished,
And you hope that it hasn't vanished.

Emelia Oldfield (11)
De Lacy Academy, Knottingley

Confidence

Confidence? To me, it means standing up for yourself and others.
To others, it's about showing off or becoming too confident.

Some people are scared or too afraid.
Some people have had enough and their behaviour shows their true nature.

Confidence in yourself.
Confidence in others.
It's important to learn that no one should comment
Or physically harass them just because they are different.
Whether they're from different countries, ethnicity, religion or continent.

Independence is one step to greatness.
Don't let anyone scar you for life.

Dudzai Kuture (12)
De Lacy Academy, Knottingley

Empowerment

I believe that you can be the best of yourself,
only if you can believe in yourself.

Empowered is being stronger than ever and
getting through the worst.

Now that I am better than ever
I can fly through and destroy my fears.

As I open the door, I join my difficult journey
and know that I can overcome it.

I open my mind and realise
I have so much to discover inside.

As my demons disappear I realise I have nothing to fear,
as I shine in the darkness.

As my monsters disappear,
there is nothing that I should fear.

Zain Mahmood (12)
De Lacy Academy, Knottingley

Delighting Moment

There are two things that I want to achieve,
They need a lot of patience... and effort.
But I believe in myself.
That I can achieve anything.

The first one, I have to save lives,
And this is not a game.
But the second one is completely different,
It needs a lot of observation,
Find new formulas,
Make people's lives easier.

They take a lot of time,
Many sleepless nights.
Going through many books and references,
Getting to know about reality.
But the result, it is so delighting and pleasing.

Vidita Hakeem (13)
De Lacy Academy, Knottingley

Global Warming

The cars are walking along the road.
Factories smoking like a cigarette.
People throwing rubbish in the sea.
How much more are we going to see?

We need to do something about this.
Please take a second of your time to throw your rubbish in
the bin.
Don't let people cut down trees.
If you can, don't use your car, just try a bike.

Trees give us oxygen, we need it to breathe.
If the trees start going, then so will we!
We only have one life and one world.
Save it for the children and do your best!

Alfie Steeples (13)
De Lacy Academy, Knottingley

Hayley Bradley

H appy all the time when I was with you.

A mazing days out, now only got the memories with you.

Y oung lady gone, what a tragedy.

L ove from you made me happy.

E xcited every weekend to see you.

Y outh was good, always with you

B otched brain, but that's alright.

R ecapped memories coming in at an amazing rate.

A nxiety.

D epression.

L onely.

E xpired heart.

Y our life matters.

Mollie Jo Chapman (12)
De Lacy Academy, Knottingley

Stop Global Warming

You have the power to stop global warming.
This is only just a warning.
If you don't listen to this poem,
By the time we make a move it will be all over
And all of us will be mourning.
We don't always realise but we are the monsters.
Until we take action and be told our futures
Things will keep dying.
If you think I'm lying
Then take a second to think about the things we have done.
We must act stronger
And make our planet last longer.

Reuben Holden-Clough (13)
De Lacy Academy, Knottingley

Believe

I believe that you can be the best of yourself,
Get the career you want,
Acquire what you want,
When you want.
It's just about how much you try.
I want to live in a £40 million London mansion,
A McLaren by my side,
Helping the people in need.
You just need to believe in yourself,
Even through the difficult times.
You could do anything you want,
As it's all about being happy,
Being yourself,
Because you need to believe.

Jayden Bailey (13)
De Lacy Academy, Knottingley

Confidence

Confidence is not an emotion or feeling.
It is a beast that lies in the mind.
Empowerment is the fuse.
You are the lighter.
In danger the beast that lies in your mind.
It will sprout like a tree.
Your mind will breathe a cycle of peace.
Your mind will speak great thoughts,
Reader, listen to this.
Let it stay in your mind for eternity.
In life and death.
What is better: to be born powerful or to overcome your weak nature through great efforts?

Callum Raynor (12)

De Lacy Academy, Knottingley

Almost There

You're empowered,
you're here,
your future is near.

Feel your energy go,
like a rapid river flow.
All your opponents behind you,
your thoughts tearing away from the glue.

The finish line is so close,
you feel like going into a doze.
You're almost there,
your perseverance is spreading everywhere.

You've won the race,
won first place.
Above all the cheering crowd,
there is a person, so proud.

Natalia Mekarska
De Lacy Academy, Knottingley

Dare To Dream

To stick with something for a long
period of time is a power like any other.
You don't have to be rich or poor,
you do it from being yourself.
Follow your dream to the ends of the Earth
and if you succeed,
you will open every door along the way.
Always keep believing above your mindset
until you are inspired
and then,
only then will you let go.
With a mindset like yours, no one can stop
you achieving your dreams.

Erin Norton (11)
De Lacy Academy, Knottingley

Empowered

I believe you can be your best self.
You need to have faith in yourself, to become your best self.
You need to have confidence in yourself, to become your best self.
You need to have resilience and become strong.
You need to work out who you are.
You need to be confident with all your decisions.
And only do something because you want to.
But out of all that the only thing that can make you your better self
Is if you believe in yourself.

Sophie Benn (13)

De Lacy Academy, Knottingley

Empowerment

What do you want to do?
Maybe you should try something new,
always try your best,
and you will settle in like a bird and its nest.
You might even find some friends to talk to.
As long as you are there for them, they will be there for you.
You can achieve anything,
in fact, you will achieve everything.
Never stop believing,
you will never stop achieving.
Just ask yourself every day like me,
who do you want to be?

Lewis Clark (13)
De Lacy Academy, Knottingley

Animals

Animals are magnificent creatures.
They have amazing features.
Giraffes are tall and have big spots.
Cats are small and have small paws.
Bears are fluffy and have sharp claws.
Dogs are hyper and full of joy.
Frogs are jumpy and have long tongues.
Birds are smart and are very interesting.
This is why they are always in a team.
Animals are amazing creatures.
They *all* have magnificent features.

Ellie Green (11)
De Lacy Academy, Knottingley

Confidence Poem

Confidence is resilient.
Knowing your worth.
Standing up for yourself.
Showing you're the one.
Knowing who you are.
You're worth more than a golden bar.
Your confidence should push you through.
The pressure should go down
And the confidence in you should blow others away.
You are powerful.
Be yourself.
Show yourself off.
Be brave.
Just know you will always be perfect.

Courtney Blakeston (13)
De Lacy Academy, Knottingley

Global Warming

Animals are amazing creatures.
They have lots of different features.
Some are big and some are small.
Some are short and some are tall.
Some eat leaves and some eat meat.
Some have flippers and some have feet.
Some live in deserts and others in snow.
But because of global warming they all will go.
They can't adapt and they can't grow.
It's getting warmer and melting the snow.

Lilly Myers (12)
De Lacy Academy, Knottingley

The Planet

The animals, the trees, the air we breathe
Being taken from us all and nature.
Instead being replaced with gasses and flames.
What can we do to save our planet?
There's marches, protests and yet
We are still so blind
To help these lovely creatures
And the forests and the rivers.
Give our planet the nutrition it needs,
It has done so much for you.

Bailey Smith (11)
De Lacy Academy, Knottingley

Be Yourself

B e yourself
E ven when time is rough

Y ou will always be above
O utgrow your differences
U nder any circumstance, everything is in the distance
R umours may spread
S ome people can't handle others' humour
E veryone is different
L ike love is magnificent
F ind yourself.

Caitlyn Lowe (14)
De Lacy Academy, Knottingley

Always

Let the chains run free.
Forever free.
It's not just an opportunity.
Use your life.
Use your dreams,
Let them go wild.
Rugby.
Live up to your dreams.
Use your dedication.
Use your patience.
Forever you can do it.
Make it pro.
If you stop dreaming.
You'll never know.
Strive for excellence.
Always.

Cobi Pearson
De Lacy Academy, Knottingley

Dreams

Dreams are wide,
They're bright,
Close your eyes,
Open your mind,
Look inside,
Infinite wishes,
For your mind,
It's as wise,
As you are inside,
One big blow,
There you go,
It can be more,
Than just one,
They're special,
Just for you,
They're just made,
For you.

Ellisha Sykes (12)
De Lacy Academy, Knottingley

Climate Change

Climate change is not a joke,
the air we breathe, we're about to choke.
Our trees are falling day by day,
the human race will go away.
We may have to move to the moon!
Still, we will all die soon.
There may be no next set of kids,
if we do not act on this.
So don't be greedy,
there's no planet B...

Jessica Wood (12)
De Lacy Academy, Knottingley

Empowered

Don't give up
you can do it,
chase your dreams,
push through it.

Right now,
you are here.
Please do not
feel the fear.

Wake up
tomorrow,
feel refreshed,
not sorrow.

Your imagination,
can be your destination.
Don't give up, you can do it.

Thomas Clarke (11)
De Lacy Academy, Knottingley

If Just For A Day...

If just for a day I had the powers to change someone's life,
I would
I'd give those who don't have any confidence
The ability to stand up and speak for themselves
And not fear being themselves.
You shouldn't care what other people think about you,
Be yourself.
Be unique.

Abigail Mitchell (13)
De Lacy Academy, Knottingley

Stephanie

Stephanie is inspiring, confident, resilient
When I struggle, she's there to help
We are respectful to each other
We do a lot of things together
She is always up for doing anything.

She really inspires me even though
She's my own sister

She really is the best.

Sophie Spence-Hirst (13)
De Lacy Academy, Knottingley

Empower

E qual rights
M en and women should get the same
P ositivity is most important
O ur Earth is changing because of selfish people
W e are all different, no one is the same
E very person should get the same
R ight to remain equal.

Lennon Hicks (11)

De Lacy Academy, Knottingley

Being A Pro Player

Being a pro player takes work.
The days fly by, still nothing.
More tournaments come, still no luck.
Last tournament I play,
I try my best, I get 120 points.
10 more to go.
Will I win?
I finally win,
I shout in joy as the last minutes come to an end.

Kieran Halligan (12)
De Lacy Academy, Knottingley

Science

S cience is amazing
C an you believe it is dazing?
I n your opinion it would be bad
E xactly like the projects you do with your dad
N ever-ending possibilities
C apabilities all change the outcome
E very reason why science is amazing.

Riley Deakin (13)
De Lacy Academy, Knottingley

I Wish...

I wish I could be someone
Not just a kid in class
Be known to help people through life.
And have a nice one of my own.
I want to be important
Have an effect on the world
And have my stories told.

Colby Platt (11)
De Lacy Academy, Knottingley

Empower

E ducate others

M aturing

P ositivity

O vercome fears

W orking on improvements

E mbracing yourself

R eassuring yourself.

Alfie Thompson (13)

De Lacy Academy, Knottingley

I Am Dark

A darkness so great it overwhelms,
such great deceit that overcomes your will to continue.
But you do.
The mask that you pull over me,
to hide me from the outsiders,
to hide me from yourself.
And I beg of you to free me;
I spring on you unannounced.
I attack you from within
until you feed me your sorrow.
You seem to possess a hatred for me,
deep-rooted just the same as me.
But I will not release you -
I will never release you -
from my grip of darkness

But there is light breaking through,
it shatters my intensity.
It is laughter and friendship,
blinding, torturous,
it carves up the hateful darkness that I have paved for you.
It sears my soul.
And I struggle
and you thrive
it becomes easier for you to use,
the mask that you pull over me,

the smile that you wear.
So great it overwhelms me,
such great power it overcomes me.

I am laid bare before you,
before the outsiders,
before your world.
They attack me,
leeching my darkness,
truth tainting my deceit.
And now it is I who possess strong hatred for you.
I who clings to the surface,
unwilling to let go.
It is you who releases me.
And I am set alight to burn.

Simply the shattered ashes of a darkness that was
overcome.

Isobelle Hennessey (14)
Edgbarrow School, Crowthorne

That Wasn't Me

You say I'm fine but that's not true,
They now think it was me, not you.
I know when you lie, you tell me you're my friend,
But all you do is get rumours about me to spread.

I curse, punch and shout,
Without even knowing what it's about.
Only I know the truth,
That wasn't me, it was you.

You're a shadow in my head,
You might as well be under my bed.
You make me dream about horrible things,
Nasty, upsetting, horrible things.

What's worse, you say I had control of what I dreamt,
But when it comes to control I'm at zero percent.
Only I know the truth,
That wasn't me, it was you.

Oh, I hate you,
I hate you so much!
You are the only thing I'd *really* want to punch.
Both of us know the truth, it wasn't me, it was you.

A few years ago, no one knew you were here,
But now that they do, I'm very glad to hear.

Now everyone knows the truth,
That wasn't me, it was you.

They have a name for you now, they made it somewhere
around September,
Oh! I think they called you Autism, now I remember.

Isabel Groves (11)
Edgbarrow School, Crowthorne

Life As A Girl

I shouldn't be afraid to walk the streets at night,
but still I am.
I shouldn't be pressured to show skin,
but still I am.
'You shouldn't hide everything'
'You have a lovely figure show it off'
But if I do that I get:
'Cover up, no one wants to see that'
'You show too much skin'
'You'll distract the boys'
How am I supposed to please myself
When I'm so focused on pleasing everyone else?

We get sexualised for almost everything we do.
'She tied her hair up, you know what that means'
How life would be different if I was born in 1992 instead of
2000s.
We're pressured to grow up quicker than ever before.
Not just for us but for other people.
If you don't you get called 'childish',
but if you grow up too quick you get told you wasted your
childhood.
Where does it stop? Where is the change?
Is there one?
Or does it all stay the same?

Caitlin Hickey (13)
Edgbarrow School, Crowthorne

Pigmentation

Why is the melanin level in someone's skin important?
'They will not be judged by the colour of their skin but the content of their character'.
Yet years later, what has changed?
Harmful stereotypes are made...
people are still discriminated against, even today.
But why should they live in fear; in fear of their family's lives, in fear of their own?
The people who should protect us,
some live in fear of, and what does that show about us?
About humans?

We should be thought of as the same,
because at the end of the day, race doesn't change a thing.
Where you were raised, how you were raised, the people who raised you,
have more of an effect on you than the pigmentation of a person's skin,
how do we think that could even possibly change the way a person behaves,
all these stereotypes just keep us in a cage.
So what does that show about us?
About humans?
There should be one race: the human race.

Anwyn Howley (13)
Edgbarrow School, Crowthorne

I Used To Be...

I used to smile all the time,
But now I'm gloomy,
I used to be sitting at the front of the class smiling and
waving,
Now I'm at the back trying to be avoided,
I used to love myself,
But now I'm insecure and care what people think,
I used to have a boyfriend,
But now I know I'm gay and don't know what people will
think,
I used to be smart,
But now I'm failing most classes,
I used to look nice,
Now I hate myself,
I used to have a real smile,
Now it's just fake.

Abigail Turner (12)
Edgbarrow School, Crowthorne

Panic

Panic flooded my head
My worries climbed over
I didn't think I could talk to anyone about it
But I was wrong
Sometimes I feel alone
But I am not
Family, friends, teachers
I am me.

Meah Godwin (11)
Edgbarrow School, Crowthorne

The Jar

The jar is quite full
Its blue mixture swooshes around
It lets out some love

When you ignite it
The room fills with emotion
and nothing compares.

Appreciate your family.

Anya Agarwal (11)
Edgbarrow School, Crowthorne

Me

What does it means to be me
Just a student who attends the UTC?
An ordinary boy who loves his family?
A loyal supporter of Port Vale FC?
Or so much more than that

Usually calm and collected like the oceans and seas
But me in a bad mood you don't want to see
That's me

Like a lion I value courage and loyalty
Especially when it comes to my friends and family
That's me

I'm proud to be a Brit and Northern Irishman too
In Cumbria I've lived my whole life through
That's me

I love walking my dog through nature and seas
My terrier Cedric means the world to me
That's me

F1 and football are passions for life
You can't beat the stands on a cold Tuesday night
That's me.

Derren Tyson (14)
Energy Coast UTC, Lillyhall

Who Am I To Them?

Glistening brightly like a ruby gem,
Staring at my reflection in the mirror,
Who am I to them?
Who am I to them?

Furry, small and cute,
Just like a koala,
Sometimes too soft and sensitive,
Kindness is the most significant feature.

Laughs, tears and smiles,
The light to my darkness,
Family and friends,
Who would I even be without them?

A bucket of stress and worry,
Thoughts and feelings running through my head,
Why worry?
If you've done the very best you can, worrying won't make it
any better.

Striving for something big and better,
Disadvantaged due to my gender,
Like a koala running for a bit of bamboo,
Just a young girl wanting to succeed.

A small town,
Memories, good and bad,
The dream to help others,
Grow and achieve.

So I ask myself again,
Who am I to them?
But why does it matter who I am to them?
I am me.

I am me.

Ruby Haile (14)
Energy Coast UTC, Lillyhall

Me Being Me

I am me,
I wouldn't change a thing,
My school, my home, my family,
They are all great,

Each and every day my family,
Empower me to do great things each day,
My dog cheers me up when I'm down,
My brother is a pain most of the time,
But every once in a while he is funny,

My sports, football, golf, running
Are my places I go most of the time,
I improve every day,
Achieving goals I set for myself,
Every day,

My bar in the garden is where I go,
To watch my favourite football team,
golfers, boxers it's where I'm watching them,
My football is where I enjoy most of my time,
After school.

Callum Bell (14)
Energy Coast UTC, Lillyhall

See-Through

I walk past to mirror
To see myself staring
Who am I to them?
Who am I to myself?

The people on the streets can't see me for who I am
They see me for my skin,
My clothes
And my car

The ones I hold close, cherished and near
They know who I am, not just how I appear
They can see past blemishes, blights and blotches
They can see through the false faces we wear,
They see through the facade we fear yet keep so near

To them you are not a mirror, reflecting the world,
To them you are a pane of glass,
Pleasant as a pearl.

Alfie Cape (13)

Energy Coast UTC, Lillyhall

Me, Myself And I

Me, myself and I,
A solo ride for life,
Nothing like savages digging deep like a knife,
Some people cold as ice, some people cold as ice,
But me, myself and I,
Calm like the ocean,
Because I've got me for life,
With family's support and hard work,
My future is bright,
Shining like burning like a light in a dark room,
Other people's future being wasted and swept away with a
dusty old broom.
But my hard work and family support will pay off,
Because one day my future will be bright,
Like a burning light.

Oliver (14)

Energy Coast UTC, Lillyhall

Improvement

G - I think I am a Generous person.

R - Recently I started a new school.

A - A new school is a fresh start and I can try my hardest from now on.

C - I have gained more Confidence in the few weeks I have been here.

I - I am more independent and get on with my work on my own.

E - I have Enjoyed every day I have been here and looking forward for the upcoming years.

Gracie (14)

Energy Coast UTC, Lillyhall

My Dog

For the wag of the tail, and the bark of hello,
to no other friend I would ever go,
to whisper my fears and lick away tears,
to run and jump and to twirl around
there's no better friend I have ever found.

Bobby Ennis (14)
Energy Coast UTC, Lillyhall

97%

They taught me words from "Still I Rise",
That I should let my power whirl,
But still you tell me pretty lies
On the truth of being a girl.

"Pull down your skirt!"
"Put a jacket on!"
Are the words we always hear,
When really they should be,
"Never live your life in fear."

Our eyes are always watching
When the streets are getting dark,
Alone and feeling helpless
In the middle of a park.

While a man walks near me in the night
I pretend to send a text,
Panic running through my mind
Worrying what will happen next.

97% of females,
And I wonder, "What is being done?"
As women, we need safety,
So we can shine without the sun.

Hannah Hughes (14)
Highcliffe School, Highcliffe

The Empowerment Wand

Wave away prejudice
Wave away racism
Wave away sexism
Wave away homophobia

Wave in equality
Wave in kindness
Wave in respect
Wave in tolerance

Wave away hate
Wave away despair
Wave away fear
Wave away anger

Wave in love
Wave in hope
Wave in confidence
Wave in calm

Wave away war
Wave away slavery
Wave away greed
Wave away shouting

Wave in peace
Wave in freedom

Wave in generosity
Wave in listening

Be empowered
Be the wand
Wave away wave in
Use your power

Alex Hughes (11)
Highcliffe School, Highcliffe

Nature

Nature is natural and you should think about it eternally.
Explore outside and observe the animals.
Breathe and sniff pink, blue and yellow flowers,
Perfumed sweet as cotton candy.

Have a bright future breathing the cool and refreshing air.
Look at the bright beaming sun.
Soak and absorb the heat.
And beat the heat.

Each time you go outside, your quality of life becomes
preferable
Your mental health improves.
Your stress is discharged.
Eventually day to day your mood will change forever.

Feel free as a bird to go outside.
Meet new people, laugh, talk and enjoy life.
Make friends and be humble against others
Open the curtains, peek at the view and the beauty of
sunlight.
Open your eyes to a new world
Come off the gadgets and go for an adventure.

On your way, discover how and why global warming is
emerging around the world.
If you have finished using your phone, please turn it off.

Ashea Letts
Highshore School, Camberwell

A World Beyond Ours

Sometimes when I am on my own,
I imagine myself in a world where everything is perfect
without any rules or responsibilities.
I picture myself in the woodlands with many animals, many
flora and fauna, Where anything can be free, regardless of
where they came from.
The ocean's waves seep through the sandy terrain as I
voyage at the tropical lands of freedom.
The fishes and coral shine their inner colour as they vibrate
like true stars.
As the day ends
I make myself comfortable to see the never-ending sky of
stars as they zoom past the darkened horizon.
No matter what anyone can say or do
I will always be in my dream world even my friends can
come along.
By the time I come back
The world is a place accepting of everyone and everything.
Believe in my words that anyone can dream
But only the fearless can be great.

Molly Grealish (16)
Highshore School, Camberwell

George Floyd 25 May 2020

George Floyd was attacked in America by two police officers.
One of them knelt on his neck wrongfully.

The police should treat everyone the same.
Stop treating black people differently!

Police should handle situations better.
Police should stop being so aggressive towards black people.
People feel frustrated because the police are not respecting black people in America.

I would like my voice to be heard because I want change to happen.
I feel frustrated, angry and upset
When I see people, who look like me
Being mistreated by people who are meant to protect us.

Tiarnie Porter (16)
Highshore School, Camberwell

My Choice

Choice is the way you want things to be.
Something you want to do and not others.
The choice to take your own path in life.
The way you want to live.
My choice is to be happy, healthy, fulfilled and successful.
I don't like listening to the news, full of sadness
I have enough sadness in my life.

Harry Lorraine-Grimes (16)
Highshore School, Camberwell

My Pokémon Cards

I think my cards are really cool
I even take them to my school.
Some are orange, purple and green
With different animals to be seen.
I like my cards, they make me happy
When I get new ones, I get clappy.
At Christmas I get brand-new ones
They bring me lots and lots of fun.

Annabelle Allen (14)
Highshore School, Camberwell

My Choices

C hoose to be independent.
H ow I like to go to my friend's house.
O ne day I will be a waitress
I choose my own clothes.
C hoose my own routes to school.
E ach day I go to the park.

Casey
Highshore School, Camberwell

What Is This?

What is this?
This jabbing pain in my heart.
Something's amiss.
Like I'm back at the start.

Back where I came from,
Everything undone.
Now I can't see him,
Can't help but feel it.
Like a scene from a film,
He's right there,
But I can't have him.

Those ocean eyes,
I recognise.
And that awkward toothy smile
From days gone by.

Thoughts run wild
As they enter my mind.
But one in particular seems to reside:
The first time I laid eyes on you, I didn't think my heart
Would see it through.
But here we are.

Years ahead.
I'm as good as dead

To you.
You've got no clue.

Those messy tresses.
Your facial expressions.
The very dimples on your cheeks.
They're all so familiar to me.
There's a lilt in your laugh.
Yes, I know it seems daft.
But your voice is melodic.
I know this sounds neurotic,
I don't care
You left me threadbare.

Once upon a time there was 'you and I',
But you lied
And I cried
And our love died.
I used to be so happy
Because there was no one better than 'he'.

What happens when 'the one' turns out to be a cheat?
What happens when two become one?
When us becomes me?
You had your fun,
Now find the next one.
Join the back of the queue.
I no longer need you.

Alana Forsythe (16)
Magherafelt High School, Magherafelt

Hi, My Name Is Ed

You say
Don't eat that.
You're too fat.
That's unhealthy.
That's bad food.
You're a failure.
You say
That you're my friend.
That you will never leave me.
You remind me
Seeing the scales go down makes you happy, doesn't it?
You say
Skipping one meal won't hurt.
It's no big deal.
It's the only way to feel happy.
It's the only way to be perfect.
Look at that girl with millions of followers.
She's happy, isn't she?
But, deep down I know
You're not really my friend.
Even though
In ways you're right -
It did make me happy.
Well, it used to.
Losing weight.

The feeling of having control.
But, the other things.
The things you didn't tell me about.
Make me wish
I had never become friends with you.
The guilt after every crumb
That enters my mouth.
The constant dizziness.
The loss of hair.
The risk of having no children.
Having no energy.
Being cold all the time.
Ruining relationships
With people that care.
The fear you gave my parents.
The thought of having to bury their daughter.
When I became friends with you,
You took away my freedom.
My happiness.
I wish I had ignored you,
When you first said:
Hi, my name is Ed.

Chantelle Logan (16)
Magherafelt High School, Magherafelt

Locked In A Cage

It feels like I'm locked in a cage where I can't -
get out.
The monster is full of total rage burning inside me.
The constant fear building up inside me
the more I hear the words
"You'll be fine."
It's more than I can take.
But I'm not fine. Nor will I be.
The voice in my head is bright -
always controlling me.
I want friends, but I can't hang out.
I tell them it depends.
Does it though?
My eyes glisten from the tears welling up inside them.
all the stupid lies I tell to get out of
going places -
with bad memories.
The cage might have an open door now,
leaving is an option, yet I can't seem to leave.
My poor friends, wondering why I got so distant.
Zoning out, overthinking every little thing I've done.
Wondering if
I embarrassed myself.
Wondering if
I said something to hurt someone.

Always feeling like an inconvenience to people, just by -
standing there.
I always worry that I am annoying.
I hurry to end conversations in fear.
I can't wait until,
finally,
someday,
I can leave this cage for good.

Lucy Arrell (13)
Magherafelt High School, Magherafelt

To Our Generation

To our generation,
these few years have been tough.
We have been through the smooth and the rough,
but I have a few things that I want you to know.

To our generation,
be like the sun.
Even though it is alone, it shines bright.
Be like the sun even when people have left you
and you feel like there's nothing left.

To our generation,
the right person will come. At the right time.
They will be the sun in your storm.
The right person will come. At the right time.
They will be the traffic lights in your road
and let you cross.

To our generation,
be the shepherd to the sheep.
Do not leave anyone out.
Be the shepherd to the sheep.
When you know one is lost,
go and find them.

To our generation,
even if someone is being mean to you,
be nice to them.
Kill them with kindness.
Even if they are your worst enemy.
Kill them with kindness.

To our generation,
we have been through a lot.
We will go through more.
But, if we do these few things,
we can make this world a better place
and fill it with grace.

Grace McCormick (13)
Magherafelt High School, Magherafelt

Think About It

Bullying,
it happens every day.
People talk about the consequences, but they never see them.
Life is easy, they say.
But it's not. Life isn't.
I stick a smile on,
dry my tears,
"Life is great!" I repeat to everyone.
People talk about the problem,
but victims won't speak out.
Victims sit there.
The bully's words cutting deeper than a knife.
Some victims start habits.
Some bad, some good.
If you look, you will only see good.
Take time to look and let people talk to you.
Comfort them through their rough times.
"Sticks and stones may break my bones but words will never hurt me."
Whoever said that needs slapped!
Words hurt! Even if it was 'just a joke'.
Think before you speak.
Would those words hurt you?
If they would, shut your mouth.
Sit back and leave that person alone.

Maisy Lee (12)
Magherafelt High School, Magherafelt

My Superpower

Who says having a superpower isn't real?
I have a superpower.
Some days it's good, but some days it's bad.

I may say hurtful things, I don't mean
To, *please* forgive me.
If I hit you, I don't mean to,
Please forgive me.

When my tics are bad I feel like my body belongs to
someone else.
My eyes flicker. My hand hits hard,
My neck jerks until the pain is overpowering
Strangers. *Please* don't stare at me or give me dirty looks.
It's not me, my superpower is in control.

Please don't be mean to me.
I try to control my tics, but the urge just takes over my body.
Some days, the pain and exhaustion is so bad I just want to
sleep all day.

But,
With the help of my friends, family and teachers.
My confidence is growing every day.

Gail Huey (13)
Magherafelt High School, Magherafelt

To The Entitled

To the entitled,
Yes, we run the same distance,
But as you run on a smooth pavement,
We run through a thorn bush.
To the entitled,
Yes, we both climb the same wall,
But as you use the steps,
We use the rocks.
To the entitled,
You claim to give a voice to the voiceless,
But you speak for the people,
Who took our voices away.
Equal rights need not be earned.
They should be given.
Blood should not be shed,
For the oppressed to be seen as people.
The suffragettes got votes for women.
Rosa Parks and Martin Luther King Junior,
Got civil rights.
Equality comes closer to the norm every day.
So,
To the entitled.
We are empowered.
We fight the good fight.
And eventually,

All you have done will come to light.
And after,
Will come our equal rights.

Leah McFadden (13)
Magherafelt High School, Magherafelt

It's All Gonna Be Okay

Hey there past me, I hope you're doing swell.
Actually, I know for a fact that you're not really doing well.
But it's all gonna be okay.
I know that just recently, Great-Grandpa died.
And, I know for a fact that you screamed and you cried.
But it's all gonna be okay.
I know that sometimes, you'll be flooded in fear.
And, I know for a fact that sometimes, you even shed a tear.
But it's all gonna be okay.
Sometimes you feel like you're left in the dark.
And there's nothing to help you, not even a spark.
But it's all gonna be okay.
And last but not least, you feel like you're alone.
And you feel like you know that, right down to the bone.
But it's all gonna be okay.

Ethan Wilson (12)
Magherafelt High School, Magherafelt

Hard Times

If anyone reading this
Is going through a hard time
I hope I can cheer you up
With some simple, easy rhymes.
It's okay to be worried,
And only human to be sad,
Whenever you feel either of those
Try talking to your mum or dad!
If you're feeling anxious,
About a meet-up or a test,
There's nothing to worry about,
You'll only worsen it with stress.
If you're feeling useless,
You were given life for a purpose,
So don't waste your time
Feeling bad for broken urchins.
You are really special
There's no one else like you
If someone else can do something,
You can do it too!
Thank you for staring
At this old piece of wood
I hope what I said,
Can make you feel good!

Tyler Smyth (13)
Magherafelt High School, Magherafelt

Don't Be Afraid

Listen to me here.
Don't you dare
let anyone boss you around
or pick on you.
Stand up for yourself.
Don't be afraid.
If you're getting bullied at school,
stand up to the bully.
Don't let him dictate to you or make you
do something you
don't wanna do.
If you're feeling peer pressure.
Don't be one bit afraid
to stand up for yourself.
Don't let anyone peer pressure you.
You are a beautiful person.
You have such a caring and thoughtful heart.
You are amazing
because you are yourself.
Stay positive.
Don't be afraid.

Matthew Linton (12)
Magherafelt High School, Magherafelt

The Environment

Climate change, look what we're doing.
The homes of the polar bears are going.
Take a walk.
Have a talk.
Be like Greta and put the world to shame.
After all, we are to blame.
The sea was blue.
Now that's not true.
The hands of man destroying the land.
Rhinos, pandas, tigers, leopards,
In captivity.
To give us an activity.
This is not how these animals should live.
They should be free to see what the world can give.
But because of us and how we live in
A world full of sin.
It should go in the bin.

Grace Jones (13)
Magherafelt High School, Magherafelt

Soul

As bland as soaked rice water,
I'm not interesting,
like the girls in the movies or books.
I have no hunger for adventure,
no desire for love.
There's a slight edge to my features,
a lifted hump on my nose.
A drag to my lips
that leaves me unattractive.
I've spent much of my life trying to mean something.
Trying to be the main character
in a story that wasn't mine.
After years of trying to act the main part,
I've decided,
the narrator will suit me just fine.

Hollie Gilmour (16)
Magherafelt High School, Magherafelt

Self-Doubt

They say to love another,
you must first love yourself.
But it's not that easy, is it?
How do you love yourself?
She's too skinny. She's too fat.
She should eat more.
She needs to cover up.
These words haunt me.
The feeling at the pit of my stomach
when I look in the mirror
and don't see a model.
Am I pretty?
Oh, I wasn't invited... again.
Why don't they like me?
Am I too loud? Too weird?
What do they see when they look at me?

Ella Clark (12)
Magherafelt High School, Magherafelt

Chains

Dear future me,
I feel like I'm trapped
by the chains that bind my mind.
The infection that has decided
the collection of infatuation
with the one I love.
The chains that bind me
will no longer stand.
I hope you understand.
You can escape and aspire to be a better person.
Your own desire.
I will get myself together.
Or should I?
As they say;
birds of a feather flock together.

Sienna Smith (15)
Magherafelt High School, Magherafelt

Dear Future Society

Dear future society,
I ask that one day, people are not judged by the colour of their skin.
I ask that one day, little girls aren't married off to old, evil men.
I ask that one day, women can decide what they do with their bodies.
I ask that one day, people can freely speak up about their trauma and not be shamed for it.
Dear future society,
What I am asking for, is change.

Rose Nicholl (15)
Magherafelt High School, Magherafelt

Empowered

E veryone should feel empowered.

M otivated to do their best.

P ositive mindsets will help you

O vercome the challenges you meet.

W ith confidence, courage and compassion,

E verything is achievable.

R ewards are earned with perseverance,

E ndowed to those with determination,

D etermination to be empowered.

Sophie Neill (13)

Magherafelt High School, Magherafelt

Self-Confidence

S chool is a place that I love to be,
E volving into the person that I've always wanted to be.
L earning so much that I never knew.
F un times with friends, some old and some new.

C omputer science is a fun lesson,
O rganising my stationery before each session.
N ever wanting to be late and always on time,
F antastic work on the page from my mind.
I 'm feeling more confident every day,
D oing work, trying hard come what may.
E ach page has new work and challenges me,
N othing can ever stop me from being the best I can be.
C ontinuing to work hard and being independent,
E very day that I'm here is being well spent.

Eleni Marangos (11)
The Adeyfield Academy, Longlands

Bullying And Anxiety

Stepping into the school,
Thunderstorms in my mind,
Afraid to be in the social crowds,
I try to fit in,
With the people of the school.
It is hard,
I feel alarmed,
The questions I ask...
Why can't I fit in?
Am I weird?
Am I odd?
Am I strange?
Am I different?
Am I unusual?
The list goes on and on...
And on and on...
I feel the dark,
I miss the light,
I lack confidence,
When I'm approached,
I feel distressed.
I know what is coming,
Insults, insults...
Why?
Why?

Why?
I don't know what I've done.
Nerd, nerd.
The comments being delivered to me,
What have I done?
Nothing.
Why?
It is horrible.
Geek, geek.
Why?
Why?
I don't know!
Just stop this please!
The words trapped inside my brain.
What have I done?
What have I done?
Why are you saying these nasty comments...?
What have I done?
What have I done?
An ocean of tears,
When hidden away,
From my fears,
I am afraid!
You call me names,
You take my things,
You hurt me,
I feel sad,

But I will act strong,
I will get back up,
And I will not let you ruin... my life!
You will not control me!
You will not judge me!
And you will not hurt me!
I still feel sad,
But still act strong...
And I will always aim high
With every opportunity ahead of me.
Bullying, anxiety, bullying, anxiety.
I am Robert and I am me!

Robert Vinyard (14)
The Adeyfield Academy, Longlands

Adeyfield School

A deyfield is the best school in the world.

D ays fly past when you are having fun.

E xciting lessons waiting every day.

Y ou make Adeyfield better every second.

F abulous form time in the morning.

I ntense practicals in science.

E ducation, the best one in Hemel.

L ove the teachers, they are so amazing.

D ramatic performing arts (PA).

S emper quarentes.

C ool homework, fun but challenging.

H appy times here at Adeyfield.

O vens in the canteen best cookies ever.

O bsessed with the paninis.

L aughter, you can hear in every classroom.

Jack Hart (11)
The Adeyfield Academy, Longlands

I Have A Dream

"I have a dream"
Is what Martin Luther King once said,
The many ways this quote could be taken spin in my head,
However to me these four words,
Are not as simple as they may seem,
They work together to create a much bigger scheme,
Of meaning.
I take it as a long-lost calling,
For my 'silly' dreams to be taken seriously,
Without the fear of my inevitable falling,
Because it's not as inevitable as it may seem,
So why not chase that 'silly' dream.
I take it as my sign to fight,
For my ambitions and my future life,
If I work hard enough,
If I just put in more effort,
Then who knows, that fight,
May cause those ambitions to alight.
I take it as a deeper message,
It means more than just four words,
As this quote a lot more to its passage,
Because look at what he did with these words,
These four lousy words,

He changed so many lives of Americans today,
So I take these words in high regard and pray,
That my silly dreams come true someday.

Jenna-May Botha (13)
The Adeyfield Academy, Longlands

The Creative Side

Have you ever wondered
What it's like to be free
To make your own choices
And to live in glee?
You create works of art
You create walls of steel
You create your favourite places
To keep as a memory
The creative side is amazing
It allows so much freedom and so much fun
It allows you to be flexible
To let your mind wander on its own
You can be alone
You can be with friends
Whatever you want
The creative side is always there
You could be indoors
You could be out in the sun
You could be energetic or bored
Yet it still stays there
It gives you power
Just being alone with your thoughts
No one to bother you
And no one to talk
Have you ever wondered

What it's like to be free
To make your own choices
And to live in glee?

William Douthwaite (13)
The Adeyfield Academy, Longlands

Days Of Horse Riding

When I'm horse riding,
I feel the breeze flowing across my face,
Going at a wondrous pace,
Trotting through the field,
Now my true happiness is revealed.
When I'm horse riding,
I canter through the course,
No mistakes being caused.
My horse may be lazy,
But it is also very crazy.
Horse riding is the best,
I could think nonetheless,
To the grooming and care,
To the wondrous dance in the school.
At the end of horse riding,
I lead to the fields and say goodbye,
Remembering the day that went by.
The day I had then,
I'm getting ready to go again.

Samuel Lewis (13)
The Adeyfield Academy, Longlands

Halloween!

Inside the houses excitement brews,
What costume will they choose?
They carve their pumpkins with delight,
With plans to trick or treat that night!
Outside in the street,
The ghosts and witches meet.
The pumpkins sit by the windows snarling and sneering,
Dripping with seeds, as midnight is nearing!
The lights begin to glow as the moon takes its toll,
The trick-or-treaters arrive with their buckets of candy,
The spooky shadows in the street do not look like someone
I'd like to meet.
Midnight arrives, stirring fear,
I cannot wait to do it again next year!

Rudy Jawara (11)
The Adeyfield Academy, Longlands

What Are Choices?

Choices are those voices,
And those voices are inside your head,
Even though you've said,
We have a dread,
That one day everything will be unsaid.
The answer is unknown,
But we have grown,
Even though we are not alone,
Choices are still being shown.
Is it this way or that way?
Is it tomorrow or today?
But either way we'll have to pay,
Because is it that way or this way,
Or is it today or tomorrow?
But we won't refuse,
We may get confused,
But we will always choose,
The spoken voice in your head will give you that view.

Layla Brown (13)
The Adeyfield Academy, Longlands

I Will Be Okay

The thing that empowers me most
Is my family and friends,
So read this poem that I wrote
From the beginning until the end.
With my precious family
Sat there by my side,
Speaking words of comfort
Loud and clear with pride.
They always encourage me
To be the best I can possibly be
And to follow my dreams
No matter how crazy they might be.
To be myself is what they say
Every sunny or rainy day
And that not all days will go my way
But in the end I will be okay.

Isabel Fallon (11)
The Adeyfield Academy, Longlands

Human Rights

We are all human beings we need rights
We don't need to get into petty fights
We need to stand up and remember those hard nights
For race, gender equality and much more
Rights for every human being
We don't need the wars and claws
Can we make the world as peaceful as the stars at twilight?
We strive for democracy, freedom and inclusivity
We have the right for life
The right to be free
The right for expressing our own opinions
So why are we silenced?

Nabila Khan (12)
The Adeyfield Academy, Longlands

Choice

Choice is a wonder, never a desire,
it's a miracle to think for yourself.
Never let anyone choose your fate,
you choose your own way to follow.
Don't listen to what everyone says,
you can choose any way to go.
No one has to manipulate you,
follow your heart in what it says.
Everyone can be your friend,
but can use you to listen to them.
Learn your own way, choose your own path,
don't believe what everyone says to you.

Vanesa Bartko (11)
The Adeyfield Academy, Longlands

Our World

The world is better when you love it.
The beauty of animals,
The beauty of the stars.
The beauty of nature is what sits in my heart.
What we take for granted
What we step on every day,
The Earth is alive not just on display.
What we spit on, and sometimes hate,
Is what we should love and what is great.
I hope you found this message inspiring.
Now get up, go out and start admiring.

Jessica Hinks (11)
The Adeyfield Academy, Longlands

What Empowers Me

My family make me so strong
They're so supportive
They make nothing go wrong.
The land. The sky.
They raise my confidence so high.
My family.
They're the best to me.
They help half of me be the rest of me.
No matter how rough the road.
My family will always be my stress relief.
Best believe,
I'm blessed indeed.
As if in my dreams I speak to celestial beings.

Amiyah Muzuka (11)
The Adeyfield Academy, Longlands

The Scarlet Spider

Red is all I see
As past memories haunted me
My mind overflows
And I'm drowning in red
The red in my ledger
As deep as a canyon
As thick as glue
I'm trapped
Stuck
My web is full of dew
The red in my ledger is deep
The red in my ledger is thick
Can you truly wipe out all that red
I come to my senses
Finally I'm out of my own head.

Mia Capri Newland (12)
The Adeyfield Academy, Longlands

We Were 2gether (WW2)

The glorious sun stretched out,
Every day I could feel the glorious sun on my face,
That was only a dream,
In reality, the sun was covered by ash and
Suffocating smoke and fire burning down
People's memories were turning to ash,
Every day, a bone-chilling siren came,
Every day, I hugged my child, praying and crying,
We were all painfully dying inside.

Dylan Pankhurst (11)
The Adeyfield Academy, Longlands

Choices

C hances we have to make a decision
H elp from your mindset
O ptions for you to make
I mprovising when you go wrong
C oping when you win or lose
E xpectations you have to meet
S topping when you feel you have to.

Katie Childs (12)

The Adeyfield Academy, Longlands

Up To Me

I can't be the only one
Who has not got a clue,
About where I'm heading
Or what I'm supposed to do.
Yet time won't wait for me
As days go flying by.
The one thing I can control,
Is that it's up to me to try.

Zarrah Ali (12)
The Adeyfield Academy, Longlands

Live, Laugh, Love

A haiku

Changes challenges,
Feared, favoured, loved, hated, lost.
Life, death we move on.

Skye Payne (14)
The Adeyfield Academy, Longlands

 YoungWriters®
Est. 1991

YOUNG WRITERS
INFORMATION

We hope you have enjoyed reading this book – and that you will continue to in the coming years.

If you're the parent or family member of an enthusiastic poet or story writer, do visit our website **www.youngwriters.co.uk/subscribe** and sign up to receive news, competitions, writing challenges and tips, activities and much, much more! There's lots to keep budding writers motivated!

If you would like to order further copies of this book, or any of our other titles, then please give us a call or order via your online account.

Young Writers
Remus House
Coltsfoot Drive
Peterborough
PE2 9BF
(01733) 890066
info@youngwriters.co.uk

Join in the conversation!
Tips, news, giveaways and much more!

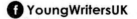 **YoungWritersUK** 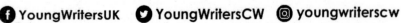 **YoungWritersCW** 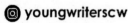 **youngwriterscw**